Maths is Childsplay

Maths is Childsplay

Jan Morrow

Longman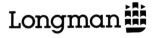

LONGMAN GROUP UK LIMITED
Longman House
Burnt Mill, Harlow, Essex CM20 2JE, England
and Associated Companies throughout the World

First published 1989
ISBN 0 582 05379 X

Set in Scantext 11pt on 12pt Frutiger

Printed and bound in Great Britain by
Courier International Ltd, Tiptree, Essex

Some of the activities in this book are also in Head Start to Learning.

Contents

Size

Colour

□ Shapes

Time

Measurement

Money

Introduction

The word 'mathematics' can produce feelings of failure, confusion and even dread in some adults. Perhaps this is because an understanding of the basic concepts behind the mathematical terms has never been fully achieved.

Mathematics in schools used to be almost totally a question of learning by rote and memorising lists of numbers with no real understanding of the meaning behind the figures. Happily, 'modern maths' now encourages mathematical discovery and understanding through practical activities.

The games and activities listed in this book aim to introduce pre-school children to a whole range of basic mathematical concepts through play, discovery and enjoyment.

For example, while making a 'Family hand print chart' children are learning to understand the terms 'bigger than' and 'smaller than'. When they play the 'Find the Treasure' game, they are physically moving 'backwards' and 'forwards' and 'counting' their steps as they do so.

The games and activities are grouped into eight areas. The first area introduces some very basic number concepts, e.g. counting, matching, sorting, sharing. The 19 games in this section use no number symbols at all, i.e. children do not need to know and recognise the written number '5' but they do tackle the concept of 'fiveness' in some detail and in very practical ways. It is important that children should have some understanding of what 'five' means before they cope with the symbol '5'. The second section introduces the notion of symbolic representation and helps children to recognise the symbols that stand for numbers.

It is important that early mathematical experience should be fun. As well as the games and activities described in these sections of the book, you should also provide plenty of opportunity for sand and water play, say lots of number rhymes with your child (e.g. One, two, three, four, five, once I caught a fish alive) and count with him at every available opportunity, e.g.

- counting the stairs as you climb them at bedtime
- counting the buttons on his coat as you fasten them
- counting the number of sausages on his plate
- counting the empty milk bottles as you put them out for the milkman

It is often in everyday experiences that the most valuble learning can take place.

The same principle can be applied to the sections dealing with the concepts of size, colour, shape, time, simple measurement and money. These areas can be developed in any order, and the games and activities can be chosen according to your child's interests.

Each game or activity is completely self-contained and because they are designed to be 'fun', children may well develop a liking for a particular game and may wish to repeat it several times. This is fine. Don't rush through the list of games. Take your time and enjoy playing them with your child.

As well as setting the activity up for their children and providing the materials, parents need to provide 'language'. It is vital that you talk about the activity or game in progress and use the appropriate words, e.g. 'too many', 'not enough', 'the same as' etc. It is through language that children can begin to understand the meaning of their experiences.

.

1 2 3 **N**umber concepts

A toys' birthday party

Collect together:

- a small number of dolls and soft toys
- a toy tea set or some old cups and saucers
- an old sheet or towel
- picnic food, e.g. a handful of raisins, a few biscuits, a jam roll
- a blunt knife
- a few birthday candles

Play the game

Ask the child to arrange a picnic birthday tea for a favourite doll or teddy, and invite two or three other toys along to the party. Lay the towel or sheet on the floor and ask the child to get the picnic ready. How many plates will the toys need? This problem is easily solved if the toys are first put into position round the towel. The child can then give one plate to each toy in turn.

Give the child the food and ask him to share it between the toys so that they all get the same. Again the child will need to match one for one.

Now for the birthday cake. Decide how old teddy is and let the child stick the candles into the cake. Count the candles as they are being placed in position. (You could even light the candles and count them as you do so, though obviously the child shouldn't handle matches.)

After blowing the candles out, sing "Happy birthday" and give the child the blunt knife to cut the cake. A long jam roll makes an excellent cake for the child to cut because it is easy for him to see how many slices he has made.

If the toys aren't very hungry, the child is usually very happy to oblige and eat the picnic for them.

Spot the odd one out

Collect together:

- groups or 'sets' of objects which have something in common, e.g.
  Apple, pear, orange, banana = fruit
  Knife, fork, spoon = cutlery
  Jumper, socks, vest, gloves = clothing

Play the game

Place a set of objects on to a table top and include one item from one of the other sets, e.g. knife, fork, spoon, vest.

Ask your child to pick the odd one out.

You can make this game harder by collecting sets of objects whose common attributes are not as obvious, e.g.
  Plastic, wooden or metal objects.
  Soft and hard objects.
  Curved and straight objects.

Feeding the lion

Collect together:

- an empty grocery box
- a pair of scissors
- a thick felt tip pen
- an old newspaper

Make the game

1 Cut the flaps from the top of the box.
2 Draw a happy lion's face on one end of the box with the felt tip pen.
3 Crush up several sheets of newspaper to form newspaper balls.

Play the game

Pretend that the newspaper balls are the lion's dinner. Ask the child to stand a short distance away from the lion and feed him, by throwing the balls into the empty box. How many balls can he get into the lion? How many fall on the floor? The child can vary the distance between himself and the box or he could have a little competition with a friend or a grown-up to see who can get the most dinner into the hungry lion.

Tall towers

Collect together:

- toy building bricks

Play the game

Have a little competition with your child to see how tall a tower you can both build out of bricks before they fall down. Count each brick as it is placed into position and count them again when the tower has fallen over. The winner is the one with the tallest tower.

Find the treasure

Play the game

This game is similar to hunt the thimble. Ask your child to go out of the room while you hide the treasure, e.g. a chocolate biscuit. When the child returns ask him to stand in the centre of the room and guide him to the treasure by giving him instructions such as, 'take three steps backwards and one step towards the window'.

Make sure he doesn't go directly towards the treasure and take the opportunity to use as many different numbers and instructions as possible. As well as 'backwards' and 'forwards', you could also include 'sideways', 'over', 'under' and 'behind'.

Sorting, sets and subsets

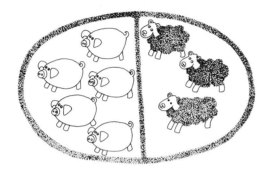

A set is simply a number of objects which have something in common. The aim of sorting is for the child the see and classify objects into sets with a common attribute. No special equipment is needed for this. Most homes are full of objects which can be classified and sorted, for example:

● If you give your child a handful of cutlery he can sort them out for you by putting all the knives together, the forks together and the spoons together;

● A bowl of toy bricks can be sorted into different colours;

● When putting the washing away, ask your child to help you sort it out into sets of daddy's socks, mummy's jumpers, tea towels, etc;

● While unloading the shopping the child could help you to sort out the tins from the packets and the fruit from the vegetables.

As you can see there are many opportunities in a child's day to play the sorting game. Gradually introduce the term 'set' at appropriate moments, e.g. "Look you have made a set of forks".

At a later stage you can begin to compare the sizes of two sets by counting or matching one set against the other. You could also draw sets of objects on to paper but when you do this remember that you should always draw a ring or 'boundary' around each set.

The idea of a set within a set (a sub-set), could also be introduced, e.g. "Look here are a set of farm animals (toy cows and pigs). If we put all the pigs together and all the cows together we have made two subsets".

If you provide your child with a drawn set of objects you could ask him to produce a subset by 'partitioning'. This simply means that he uses his pencil to separate the two (or more) different objects within the set. For example, a set of 'sweets' could be partitioned into, 2 lollipops, 1 chocolate, and 2 caramels.

In real life people spend a lot of time dividing large sets into smaller subsets. When you go out to do the shopping you don't just go out to buy 'food', you group certain foods together and divide the task into reasonably sized units.

Sorting into sets is a valuable experience for your child for he learns that things can be broken down into manageable groups or sets and he learns to compare, to divide and to classify according to a given set of attributes.

Setting the table

Setting the table for breakfast or lunch provides an ideal opportunity for counting and matching.

The child will first have to discover how many people he needs to set the table for and then count out the correct number of knives, forks, spoons, glasses, etc. If the child finds this rather difficult unaided, an adult could set out the correct number of chairs and ask him to put a knife and fork in front of each one.

Square patterns

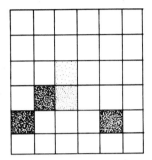 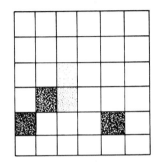

Collect together:

- several sheets of large-squared graph paper
- coloured crayons
- scissors

Make the game

1 Cut the graph paper into identically sized sheets.
2 Decide on two or three colours and colour in 5 or 6 of the squares in the centre of one of the sheets of graph paper. The squares can be coloured in any order or position but they do need to be close together. (This is quite a complicated activity, so if your child is very young, you could reduce the number of colours and squares involved.)

Play the game

Give the child the coloured square pattern, an uncoloured sheet of graph paper and some crayons.

Ask the child to make an identical pattern on her sheet of blank graph paper. To do this she will need to look at the pattern very carefully, count the number of squares and note the position of the colours.

1 2 3

Dressing paper dolls

Collect together:

- a sheet of paper, 50cm by 20cm
- scissors
- a packet of coloured, sticky-backed paper
- a pencil
- crayons

1 2 3

Make the game

1 Fold the sheet of paper in half and then in half again. Continue to do this until you have a strip of paper 10cm wide.
2 Draw a simple doll outline on the front of the strip of paper, making sure that both the doll's outstretched arms touch the folded edge of the paper.
3 Cut the doll shape out. Unfold the paper and you will find a line of identical dolls.

Play the game

Give your child the crayons and ask him to colour a set of clothes on each doll. (Alternatively he could make some clothes from the sticky paper.) Each doll should be given a set number of items, e.g. 3, although the actual items of clothing could be different for each doll.

Spot the dog

Collect together:

- 25 cards, 10cm by 5cm
- scissors
- a felt tip pen

Make the game

1 On one of the pieces of card draw a simple dog outline. Cut the dog out and use it as a template to draw the same dog on the remaining 24 pieces of card.
2 On each of the dogs draw some spots, i.e.

On four of the dogs draw one spot.
On four more draw two spots.
On four more draw three spots.

Continue to increase the number of spots by one each time until you reach six spots. Make sure that the dogs with the same number of spots are identical.

Play the game

The cards can be used in three ways:

To make a simple number line of dogs, i.e.

the first dog would have one spot and the last in the line six spots;
As the basis of a simple matching game, by asking the child to find all the dogs with one spot etc;
For a game of 'snap'.

Copy beads

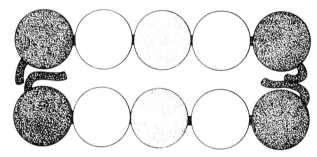

Collect together:

- large threading beads. If you can't obtain beads, paint some empty cotton reels different colours
- 2 boot laces or 2 pieces of strong string

Make the game

An adult should thread some beads on to one of the laces. They should be threaded in some sort of colour and number order. Start with something simple such as, 1 red, 1 blue, 1 red, 1 blue. Later you can move on to more elaborate variations, e.g. 2 red, 3 blue, 2 green, 2 red, 3 blue, 2 green.

Play the game

Ask your child to copy your string of beads. If he manages to do this correctly, his string of beads should be identical to yours.

All about my family

Collect together:

- a very large sheet of paper
- a black felt tip pen
- a pencil
- crayons

Make the game

1 Help the child to think about and to compare the different members of her family. She might find that there are more females than males, that everyone has blue eyes (except the dog) and that everyone but daddy likes chocolate ice-cream.
2 Some of this information can be displayed. Draw two large circles side by side on the sheet of paper and decide on which information you would like to compare, e.g. eye colour.

Play the game

In one of the circles help the child to draw the faces of all those members of the family with blue eyes (grans and grandads, aunties and uncles could be included). In the second circle draw the faces of all those family members with brown eyes.

Count up the faces in the first 'set' and the faces in the second 'set'. Which 'set' has the most faces?

Picture matching

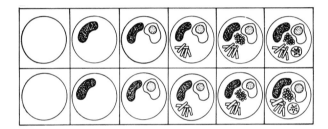

Collect together:

- 13 pieces of card, 10cm by 10cm. (One of these can be used for making templates.)
- scissors
- a pencil
- a felt tip pen

Make the game

1 Decide on a theme for a picture, e.g. a dinner, a farmyard, a vase of flowers.
2 If your theme is a 'dinner',

On the first two cards draw identical plates;
On the second two cards draw the plates again but this time add a fork by the side of each plate;
On the third pair of cards draw plates, forks and knives;
On the fourth pair of cards draw plates, forks, knives and a sausage.

Continue to add more detail each time until you have used up all the pairs of cards. Templates should be used when possible as they help to keep the shapes identical.

Play the game

The cards can be used in three ways:

For a simple game of snap;
The child can be asked to find the identical pairs of cards by matching one to one;
Some of the cards can be placed in a number line, with the first card showing the plate and the last card displaying the complete dinner.

Heads to hats

Collect together:

● sheets of paper
● a pencil

Make the game

Down the left hand side of the paper draw a row of heads and opposite the heads draw a row of hats. You could include a variety of hats, e.g. a crown, a witch's hat, a top hat, etc. Make sure that there is a hat for every head.

Play the game

Give your child the pencil and ask him to see if each head can have a hat by drawing lines from head to hats.

This one to one matching game could also use:

Dogs to bones
Bees to flowers
Cups to saucers
Spaceships to moons, etc.

At a later stage you can draw more heads than hats or more bees than flowers, so that the child can discover by simple matching that there are not always enough hats, flowers, bones, etc. You can then ask the question, "How many more hats do we need to draw?"

Finding pairs

Collect together:

● 12 pieces of card, 10cm by 10cm
● felt tip pens

Make the game

Think of six pairs of objects, for example

knife, fork
bucket, spade
a pair of boots
a pair of gloves
boat, sea
egg, nest

Draw the objects on to the piece of card.

Play the game

Jumble the cards and then give them to your child. Ask your child to find the pairs. This activity will not only help the child to recognise that 'two' objects can make a pair but can also help to improve the child's vocabulary as you discuss which items belong together.

Story cards

Collect together:

- colourful felt tip pens
- strips of card 30cm by 10cm
- a ruler
- scissors

Make the game

1 Think of some simple three part picture stories, e.g.

(i) thin dog, thin dog with plate of food, fat dog

(ii) empty glass, glass under tap, full glass

2 Divide each strip of card into three equal sections and then draw the pictures on to the strips.
3 Cut the pictures out into three separate sections.

Play the game

Give the child one set of story cards at a time and ask her to put the pictures in a line and in the right order. A little help with 'sequencing' may be needed at first and you could also use it as an opportunity to talk about the words 'first', 'second' and 'third'.

Happy face biscuits

Collect together:

- round plain biscuits, for example digestives
- cream cheese
- soft margarine
- raisins
- thin slices of carrot
- thin slices of cucumber cut in half
- cress
- a knife for spreading
- a spoon for mixing
- a bowl for mixing

To make the faces

This is an ideal pre-lunch activity as the results can be eaten. Your child should first of all mix together some margarine and cream cheese which is then spread on to the biscuits.

Ask your child to create a face on each biscuit by using cress for hair, two raisins for the eyes, one slice of carrot for the nose and one half cucumber slice for the mouth.

Body pictures

Collect together:

- a large sheet of paper. A roll of wallpaper lining paper is ideal.
- thick felt tip pens
- scissors
- Sellotape

To play the game

Create a double-width length of paper by sellotaping two long sheets of paper side by side.

Ask your child to lie down on the paper and carefully draw round her outline with a felt tip pen. Use this activity to discuss what you are drawing and to introduce the idea of numbers relating to our bodies, for example, by counting her fingers as you draw round each one.

Having obtained an outline of her body your child can then add further details to the picture by drawing two eyes, one nose, two ears, one mouth, six buttons, two shoe buckles and so on.

When the picture has been finished you can cut round the outline and hang the self portrait on your child's bedroom door.

Swing counting

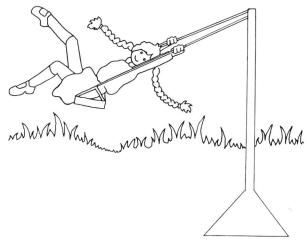

To play the game

You can use either the swing in your garden if you have one, or the swing in your local children's playground.

Suggest to your child that she should count with you how many times she swings backwards and forwards (before stopping) after just one push from you.

If there is a slide in the playground she may like to see how many times she can slide down it in two minutes or if there is a see-saw how many times she can go up and down during the nursery rhyme 'See-saw margery-daw'.

 Number symbols

An anticipation calender

Collect together:

- a sheet of paper, 40cm by 15cm
- a ruler
- a felt tip pen
- a few crayons

If your child is looking forward to an event, e.g. her birthday party, a trip to the seaside or gran and grandad coming to visit, you could make an anticipation calender. This will enable your child to tick off the days leading up to the event and she can see how close she is in time to the actual day. Start your calender a week to ten days before the event – any longer and the child will be overwhelmed by the numbers involved.

Make the game

1 Draw a ladder on the sheet of paper. (You will need to leave a 3cm space between each of the steps and you need as many spaces as there are days leading up to the event.)

2 At the top of the ladder ask your child to draw a picture of the event.

3 Starting at the bottom of the ladder write a number in each of the spaces between the steps. You need to start with the highest number first, i.e. 10, 9, 8, . . .

Play the game

Hang the calender up on the wall but do make sure that your child can easily reach it. Each day your child can colour in one of the spaces in the ladder, starting at the bottom with the highest number and working towards the top.

Button tins 1 2 3

Collect together:

- 5 identical small tins with lids or 5 identical small margarine tubs with lids
- 15 beads or buttons
- paper
- Sellotape
- a felt tip pen

Play the game

Sit next to your child and ask her to drop one button in the first tin, two buttons in the second tin, and three buttons into a third tin.

Put the lids on the tins and rather like a magician ask the child to watch carefully while you move the tins around. Ask the child to guess which tin contains one button, two buttons and three buttons. Play this game for a little while.

Stick a piece of paper on to the top of each tin. Give your child the felt tip pen and ask her to think of any marks or pictures she could make on the paper which would help her to guess what is in the tins. Children invariably make 1

1 3

1 2 3

mark or scribble on the tin containing one button, 2 marks on the two button tin and 3 marks on the three button tin. Do not mention formal number symbols at this stage.

Play the guessing game again and the child will discover that the marks she has made will help her to find the correct tins. When she has become familiar with three tins you could introduce a four and a five button tin.

At a later stage the marks can be exchanged for formal number symbols.

Matching numbers and amounts

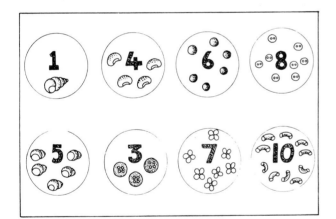

Collect together:

● a bun tray
● a collection of small objects such as buttons, small shells, pasta shapes, etc.
● circles of paper, large enough to fit snugly in the bottom of each section in the bun tray
● a felt tip pen

Make the game

Write the numbers 1-10 on ten of the circles of

paper and place each one in the bottom of a section of the bun tray.

Play the game

Give the small objects to your child and ask her to put the correct number of buttons etc. into each compartment. The child should count out loud as she drops each button into the tray.

Button cards

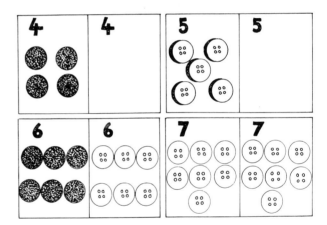

Collect together:

● 5 pieces of white card, 20cm by 13cm
● a felt tip pen
● a few buttons. They should be identical.
● a ruler

Make the game

1 Divide each card into two halves with a line.
2 In the top left-hand corner of the left half of the card, print a number, e.g. 3 and beneath the number draw three circles. As the circles need to be the same size as the buttons you are using, you can draw round the buttons.

23

3 On the right half of the card print the number 3 again. (Put it in the left hand corner, but this time don't draw any circles).

Make several cards in this way using a different number for each one.

Play the game

Give the child a card and some buttons. (Do remind little ones never to put buttons into their mouths.)

Ask the child to look at the left half of the card first and then to put a button on top of each of the circles. As she does so, count the buttons with her. Point to number 3 and remind her that there are three buttons on the card.

Ask the child to put three buttons underneath the number 3 on the right hand half of the card. This will of course be slightly harder as there are no circles to help her.

When she has successfully filled a couple of cards with your help, see if she can fill a card with buttons on her own.

A number scrap book

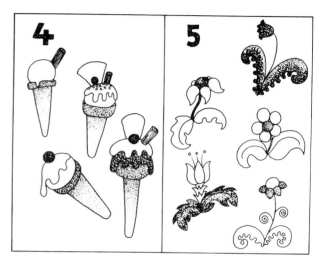

Collect together:

- a scrap book you have bought or made
- interesting pictures from magazines or comics
- glue and a glue brush
- scissors
- a felt tip pen

Make the game

At the top of each page in the scrap book print out a large number, starting with 0 and finishing with 10.

Play the game

Look through the collection of pictures and photographs and cut out any interesting objects or animals.

Sort the cut outs into 'sets', e.g.

A set of car pictures
A set of dog pictures
A set of baby pictures

Use the sets of pictures to fill the scrap book. For example page 0 would of course be left blank, page 1 could have a picture of one train on it, page 2 could have two kittens on it and so on.

Home made skittles

Collect together:

- large, empty washing up liquid bottles
- an old newspaper
- Sellotape
- a felt tip pen
- a few sheets of paper, 30cm by 22cm. (You need as many sheets of paper as there are bottles).

Make the game

1 Wrap a sheet of paper round the middle of each bottle and sellotape it into position.
2 Print a number on the front of each bottle. It is best not to go above the number 5. Beneath each number draw the appropriate number of large spots.
3 Take a sheet of newspaper and crush it tightly into a ball. Do this until you have at least five balls.

Play the game

Stand the bottles up in a group and see how many can be knocked down with the newspaper balls. The child can count how many bottles she has managed to hit; or, at a later stage, she can add up the score on the fallen bottles by looking at the numbers printed on each one and count the number of spots.

A car race game

(To make a game for two players.)

Collect together:

- 2 small toy cars
- a sheet of card or paper, 45cm by 45cm (wall paper lining paper is ideal.)
- a thick felt tip pen
- a large dice. (Obtainable from good toy shops.) Or a number spinner. (Instructions for making a spinner are included in this section.)

Make the game

On the sheet of paper draw a twisting race track, the track needs to be about 10cm wide, so that two small cars can fit side by side. With the pen, divide the track into roughly equal sections, about 8cm long.

Play the game

Put the cars side by side on the starting line. The first player spins the spinner or throws the dice and moves his car according to the number shown, e.g. if you throw a 3 you move three spaces. The winner is the one who reaches the finishing line first.

A number spinner

Collect together:

● a piece of 12cm by 12cm card
● a pencil
● scissors
● a ruler

As an alternative to a dice (large dice can be obtained from good toy shops) you might like to make a number spinner.

To make the spinner

1 Draw a large hexagon on the piece of card and cut it out.
2 With the pencil and ruler divide the hexagon into eight equal sections and print the numbers 1 to 8 in each space. If you are teaching your child the written name for numbers you could use printed words.
3 Push a sharp pointed pencil through the centre of the hexagon.

To use the spinner

Stand the pencil up on its point and twist it sharply. The score is obtained by using the number which the spinner rests on when it stops spinning.

Number boxes

Collect together:

● 10 empty shoe boxes. Most shoe shops are happy to give these away.
● 10 sheets of paper, 10cm by 10cm
● Sellotape
● a felt tip pen

Make the game

1 Remove and discard the shoe box lids. Sellotape a piece of paper on to the end of each box.
2 Number the boxes 1 to 10, by printing a large number on to the paper-covered end of each box.
3 Stand the boxes in a row with all the numbers next to each other and in the right order.

Play the game

Ask the child to fill the boxes for you with the correct number of objects for each box. The objects must also be the same in each box, e.g.

Box '1' = 1 toy farm animal.
Box '2' = 2 spoons.
Box '3' = 3 toy cars etc.

Obviously, to begin with you will need to help the child. After a couple of days, empty the boxes and start again with different objects.

Many children have a number frieze on their bedroom wall. These often have a number with a picture of an object or objects underneath. The Number boxes serve the same purpose but they are much more fun because they involve the child. She gathers and counts her own objects and she soon realises that all sorts of things can be grouped together and, unlike the pictures on a frieze, the objects can vary from day to day.

All in a row

(To make a game for two players.)

Collect together:

● 20 small pieces of 5cm by 5cm card
● a felt tip pen

Make the game

Write the numbers 1 to 10 on the pieces of card. Each number should be on two cards.

Play the game

Each player is given a card with the number 1 on it. The rest of the cards are spread out face downwards between the two players. Each player takes a turn at lifting a card.

If it is the next card in the row (i.e. number 2 comes after number 1), he keeps the card and places it in position next to his existing cards. If it isn't a card he needs he places it face downwards on the table. The winner is the one to complete the 1 to 10 row first.

A number posting box

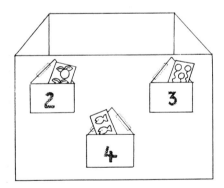

Collect together:

● 10 strong envelopes
● an empty cardboard grocery box
● a felt tip pen
● 10 pieces of card. These need to be small enough to fit into the envelopes.
● Sellotape
● felt tip pens or crayons

Make the game

1 Attach the envelopes around the outside of the cardboard box by sticking the envelope flaps on to the box with Sellotape. You should still be able to put the cards into the envelopes.
2 On the front of each envelope write a number. I would suggest using the numbers 1 to 5 initially and at a later stage you could increase the range of numbers.
3 Draw number pictures on the cards, e.g. 1 dog, 2 cats, 3 hens, etc. Your child may well enjoy helping you to draw these pictures and colour them.

Play the game

Ask the child to put the number pictures into the correct envelopes.

A pet shop picture

Collect together:

● catalogues, leaflets, magazines and old unwanted books which contain pictures of family pets
● scissors
● glue and a glue brush
● a thick felt tip pen
● a large sheet of paper

Play the game

Using the felt tip pen, divide the large sheet of paper into sections. Tell the child that each section is a cage in a pet shop and ask her to look through the magazines etc. and to cut out as many pictures of pets as she can find. Sort the cut out pictures into groups, e.g. dogs, mice, fish . . .

Assign each set of animals to a cage in the pet shop and stick the pets into position. When the last animal has been stuck into its appropriate cage or run, count the animals and see how many dogs, cats, and mice you have. Write the number clearly in the corner of each cage. This makes a particularly attractive picture for a child's bedroom wall.

Individual buns

Cooking is an excellent activity as it provides the

opportunity for counting and demonstrates to the child the practical application.

Collect together:

- a mixing bowl
- a tablespoon
- a teaspoon
- paper cake cases
- a baking tray
- self raising flour
- soft margarine
- sugar
- sultanas or currants
- milk/egg mixture (1 egg to half a pint of milk)

To make the cakes

1 Heat the oven to gas no. 6 or 180 degrees.
2 Your child should then measure out:

1 heaped tablespoon of SR flour
1 teaspoon of margarine
2 teaspoons of sugar
3 teaspoons of sultanas
2 tablespoons of milk/egg mixture

3 The ingredients should be placed all together in the bowl and mixed together well . Spoon the mixture into paper cake cases and cook for 10 to 15 minutes. (An adult should put the cakes into the oven and take them out.)

Sandpaper numbers

Collect together:

- 10 pieces of 10cm by 10cm card
- several pieces of heavy grade sandpaper
- a piece of chalk
- scissors
- glue and a glue brush

Make the game

1 Using a chalk, draw the numbers 1 to 10 on the front of the sandpaper. Each number needs to be double line thickness.
2 Cut round the outline of each number and then stick them rough side up on to the cardboard squares. (One number per square.)

Play the game

The sense of touch is most important to young children. The use of sandpaper numbers develops this sense and uses it to familiarise the child with the shape of each number.

Give the child one or two numbers at a time, ask him to feel the numbers and tell him what they are called.

When he has explored the numbers sufficiently, play the blindfold game. Cover the child's eyes, give him one of the numbers and ask him to tell you by touch which number he can feel. Take turns at playing the blindfold game and if you wish to make it a little more exciting you could award a point for each correct guess.

Magic numbers

Collect together:

- sheets of white paper
- a white candle
- a jar of very thin black paint
- a paint brush

Make the game

1 Choose some numbers that your child is working with at the moment, e.g. 1, 2, 3, 4, 5.
2 Use the candle to draw on each sheet of paper a number and a picture showing the appropriate number of objects. You will need to press down quite firmly with the candle.

Play the game

Ask the child to discover the magic number and pictures by painting gently over the wax treated paper with the thin black paint. Small children are always amazed to see the magic numbers appearing.

Plasticine numbers

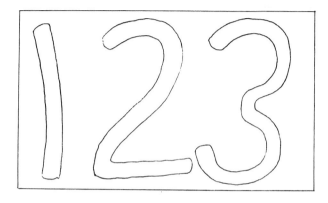

Collect together:

- 10 squares of card, 20cm by 20cm
- plasticine
- a pencil

Make the game

Using the numbers 1 to 10 write each number on to a square of card. Make the numbers as large as possible.

Play the game

Help your child to make several long plasticine 'snakes'. Help the child to use the 'snakes' to make the numbers on the cards by laying the plasticine on top of the print. If the 'snake' is a little too long or short for a particular number you can easily add to or take away some of the plasticine.

Do remember to encourage the child to form the numbers correctly, e.g. you always start at the top of the number.

At a later stage your child may be able to make the numbers without the aid of the printed number underneath.

**ize**

Grading and sorting

Collect together:

A collection of objects of various sizes. The following list gives an idea of some of the possibilities . . .

- stones from the beach or garden
- shells
- socks of all sizes
- flowers, anything from a daisy to a sunflower
- toy bricks
- soft toys – children invariably have quite a collection of teddies etc

Play the game

Give the child the collection of objects e.g. soft toys, and ask her to find the biggest and the smallest toy. Having found these ask the child to go on to sort out the rest of the toys, putting them in a line in order of size.

Matching lids

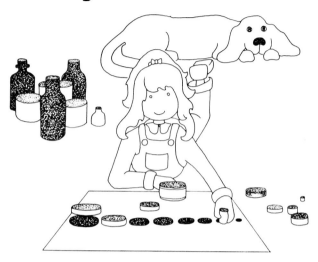

Collect together:

- 10 variously sized lids from jars and bottles
- a few sheets of coloured sticky-backed paper
- a large sheet of paper or card. The size rather depends upon the size of the lids.
- a pencil
- scissors

Make the game

1 Draw round each lid or bottle top on the sticky coloured paper to make a set of outline shapes.
2 Cut the shapes out and stick them on to the larger sheet of paper in order of size.

Play the game

Give the child the collection of lids and the sheet of coloured shapes. Ask her to match each of the lids and tops with the same-sized coloured shape.

Family handprints

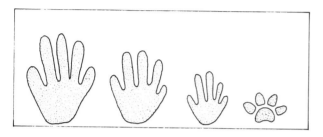

Collect together:

- a bowl of handprint paint.
  To make the paint you simply mix together wallpaper paste (without fungicide) and dry powder paint or food colouring. The mixture needs to resemble thick cream.
- a large sheet of paper
- several smaller sheets of paper
- scissors
- glue and a glue brush

Play the game

Ask each member of the household to dip their hands in the handprint paint and to make a handprint on one of the smaller pieces of paper. Even the tolerant family dog can be included in this activity.

When all the prints are dry, cut them out and arrange them in order of size on the large sheet of paper. When your child is satisfied that the prints are in the correct order she can glue them into position.

Fill the egg cup

Collect together:

- an egg cup

Play the game

Give your child the egg cup and ask him to fill it with as many different items as he can find, e.g. a grain of rice, a daisy, a paper clip, etc. The child will soon discover which objects are of an appropriate size.

If two or more children are playing this game they could have a little competition to see who can find the highest number of items.

A shoe shop

Collect together:

- as many different shoes, boots and slippers as possible
- a toy till or empty box
- a handful of real money or clean milk bottle tops
- small squares of card with various prices written on them. It is best not to go above 10p

Play the game

Help the child to prepare his pretend shoe shop. Explain that the shoes will need to be arranged in order of size, i.e. daddy's large shoes at one end of the counter and baby's boots at the other. Place the price tags in position and play shop.

Children love to try on their parents' shoes so this game has an added attraction.

Mixed up lids

Collect together:

- a collection of clean, empty jars, bottles and boxes, with lids

Play the game

Take the lids off all the bottles, jars and boxes. Mix the lids up and give them to your child. Ask her to put the lids back on to the appropriate jars etc.

To start with it might be best to limit the number of containers and lids you give to the child but as she becomes more proficient the number can be increased.

Please remember that when playing with glass containers young children should be carefully supervised.

Dogs and bones

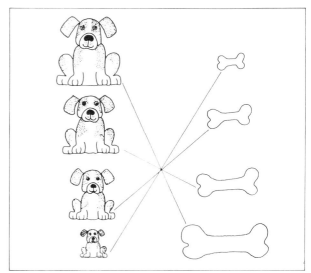

Collect together:

- a sheet of paper
- a pencil

Make the game

Draw a row of variously sized dogs down the left hand side of the paper and opposite the dogs draw a row of appropriately sized bones, i.e. a large bone for a large dog. The bones should not be in the correct order.

Play the game

Ask the child to draw a line from each dog to a bone. The largest dog should have the largest

bone. You could extend this idea and draw teddy bears with pots of honey, spaceships with moons, hens with eggs, or indeed any suitable combination of pairs.

Snake biscuits

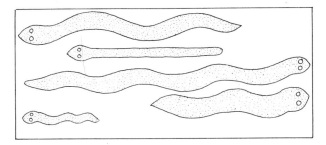

Collect together:

- 115g flour
- 55g margarine
- 80g grated cheese
- 1 tablespoon of water
- pinch of salt
- 1 beaten egg yolk
- currants
- a sieve
- a mixing bowl
- a pastry board
- a greased baking tray

To make the snakes

1 Sift the flour and salt into the bowl. Rub in the margarine and grated cheese. Gradually add the beaten egg and water.
2 Mix and knead the mixture until you have a stiff pastry.
3 Give the child lumps of the dough and ask him to roll out the mixture on a floured board until he has created long snake like shapes.

4 Carefully transfer the snakes on to the baking sheet and ask your child to add two currant eyes to the head end of each snake.
5 Bake the snakes in a pre-heated oven at 150 degrees for 15 minutes.

Making snakes like these provides you and your child with an ideal opportunity to talk about the concepts long and short, thick and thin, straight and curved, big and little.

Building a snowman

Collect together:

- a large sheet of coloured paper
- 5 circles of white paper (The circles should gradually increase in size.)
- a felt tip pen
- glue and a glue brush

To make the snowman

1 Ask your child to glue the circles (or snowballs) in a vertical line on to the large sheet of coloured paper, starting with the

largest snowball at the bottom and the smallest snowball at the top.

2 Having made the snowman's body, a face, hat, arms, and coal buttons can be drawn in position with the felt tip pen.

The Goldilocks game

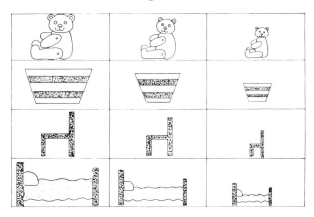

(To make a game for two players)

Collect together:

- 2 large sheets of card, 30cm by 20cm
- 24 small pieces of card – each one should be 5cm by 10cm
- a few extra pieces of card for making templates
- a ruler
- a felt tip pen

Make the game

1 With the felt tip pen and ruler divide the large sheets of card into 12 equal sections. Each section should be 10cm by 5cm.

2 In the top three sections on each card draw 3 simple bear shapes, one bear to each section - - one large, one medium and one small. (Templates will help you keep the shapes a regular size.)

3 In the next three sections (underneath the appropriate bear), draw 1 large bowl, 1 medium bowl and one small bowl. Beneath these draw 3 chairs and finally in the bottom three sections draw the three bears beds.

4 The bears, bowls, chairs and beds should also be drawn on to the individual pieces of card. Again templates will help accuracy. When you have finished doing this you should have two small cards with large bears on, two with medium sized bears on, two with small bears and so on.

Play the game

Each player takes a large card.

Lay the small cards face downwards on the table top.

The players take turns at lifting a card and if it matches a picture on the large card, they place the small card on top of the picture. If they do not need the small card they return it face downwards on the table. The winner is the first one to cover the large card completely.

 **Colour**

A colour collage

Collect together:

- old colourful magazines
- scissors
- glue and a glue brush
- scraps of material, wool and wrapping paper of the chosen colour
- a sheet of paper

To make the collage

1 Help the child to decide on a colour, e.g. blue.
2 Look through the old magazines and find pictures of blue things, such as a blue dress and a blue car. The child should cut out as many blue pictures as possible and stick them, along with any scraps of blue material, wool and paper he might have, on to the sheet of paper.

Egg box tiddly winks

Collect together:

- 2 empty egg boxes
- different coloured paints
- tiddly winks
- scissors
- a felt tip pen

Make the game

1 Cut the lids from the egg boxes and paint inside the egg cups with different coloured paints. Paint two cups red, two blue and so on.
2 When the egg boxes have dried, stand them side by side.

Play the game

Decide on a colour score system, i.e. red cups score 1 point, blue cups score 2 points etc. (You could always write the score with a felt tip pen in the bottom of each cup).

Flick the tiddly winks into the cups from a short distance away or if this is too difficult for little ones simply throw the counters into cups. The winner is the one with the highest score.

A colour table

Decide on a colour, for example green.

Together with your child look around your home and make a collection of green objects. This could include green apples, a green jumper, a green toy car, a green pencil and so on.

Create a 'green' table where the objects can be displayed. Your child can add to the green collection over a period of a few days. After a week start again with a new colour. This is an ideal way for little ones to learn their colours.

Lollipops lotto

(To make a game for two players.)

Collect together:

- 2 pieces of card, 25cm by 20cm
- coloured felt tip pens
- 10 circles of card. Make these by drawing round a 10p coin
- a 10p coin

Make the game

1 Draw 5 lollipops on each piece of card. Make the lollipop tops by drawing round the 10p coin.
2 Colour the lollipops with a variety of different colours.
3 Colour the circles of card in the same colours as you have used on the lollipops, i.e. one circle for each lollipop.

Play the game

Put the circles, colour side down on the table. The two players take turns to pick up a circle and name the colour on it. If it is the same colour as a lollipop on their card, they can cover the lollipop with the circle. A lollipop can only be covered once.

The winner is the one who covers all 5 lollipops first.

A colour scrap book

Collect together:

- a scrap book you have made or bought
- scissors
- glue and a glue brush
- old magazines, comics, Christmas cards, and pretty wrapping paper

Play the game

Each page of the scrap book should be devoted to a particular colour, e.g. the first page could be a 'red' page, the next one 'blue' and so on.

LOOK through the collection of magazines, cards, etc. and ask your child to cut out anything which has an obvious colour. The pictures can then be stuck on to the appropriate pages in the scrap book.

Colour sorting

Give your child a group of variously coloured objects, e.g. toy bricks, toy cars, Smarties, cotton reels. Ask her to sort them out for you by putting the same colours together. Talk about the colours as she does so, e.g. "That's a nice yellow Smartie. Are there any more? Are you wearing anything yellow?"

You should try to refer to different colours by name as often as possible.

Colour I-spy

Using the colours instead of the initial letter sounds of objects makes the traditional game of I-spy a much simpler game which can be enjoyed by very small children, e.g. I-spy with my little eye something which is white.

Take turns at playing the game and don't forget to pick out and use the more unfamiliar colours, such as grey, purple and silver.

Egg box Smarties

Collect together:

- A number of cut out cups from egg boxes. Paint the cups a variety of different colours, for example red, yellow, green, blue, orange, pink, purple, grey, brown.
- A handful of Smarties; or if you prefer, raisins

Play the game

Sit with your child and place the egg box cups in front of her with the cups turned upside down.

Ask your child to close her eyes tight and while she is doing so pop a Smartie or raisin underneath one of the cups

Tell her to open her eyes and find the Smartie underneath the 'purple' cup.

It is amazing how quickly children can find the correct colour when there is a Smartie as reward.

Later you can make the game a little harder by saying something like, 'Open your eyes and find the Smartie in the cup behind the yellow cup,' or 'In front of the brown cup'.

Colourful milkshakes

To make the milkshakes

Keep in your kitchen cupboard a wide variety of different food colourings. Then whenever your child wants a glass of milk he can select a colour, add a few drops to his drink, and stir up a milkshake. (Please note that many health food shops sell natural colourings.)

Not only will your child be experimenting with and discovering lots of colours but he will be making milkshakes without adding harmful sugar to his milk.

Colour patterns

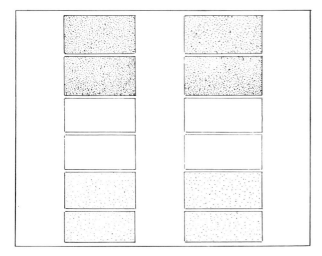

Collect together:

- an assortment of cut out paper shapes each with an individual colour, for example, red squares, black squares, yellow squares
- sheets of plain white paper
- glue and a glue brush

Play the game

To start with you can give your child an example of a repeating pattern by gluing a line of shapes on to a sheet of paper. e.g. 3 red squares, 3 black squares, 3 red squares, 3 black squares. Ask your child to copy the pattern underneath before asking her to create her own patterns using as many colours as she likes.

Colour matching

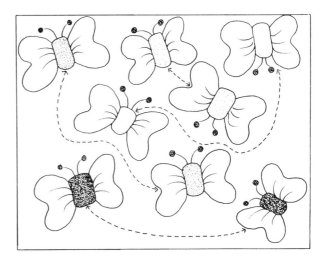

Collect together:

- sheets of paper
- coloured felt tip pens

Make the game

On each sheet of paper draw a number of identical items but colour them with different colours making sure that you have two of each colour, for example,

An assortment of different coloured balloons, 2 red, 2 blue, 2 green...
An assortment of different coloured cars, 2 yellow, 2 orange, 2 pink...

Play the game

Give your child the sheets of paper and ask her to match the colours by drawing lines (possibly using the same coloured pen) joining the same coloured objects together. For example, a red line could link the 2 red balloons.

 # hapes

Robbie the robot

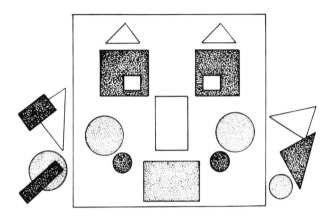

Collect together:

- 2 sheets of card, 20cm by 20cm
- scissors
- a pencil
- a ruler
- a few sheets of coloured sticky-backed paper
- a felt tip pen

Make the game

1 Draw some different shapes on to the sticky-backed paper. These might include circles, rectangles, squares and triangles. You could also make each shape in two different sizes.
2 Cut the shapes out and stick them on to one of the sheets of card. Then cut the shapes out for a second time. You should now have a collection of colourful, card-backed shapes.
3 Draw a large square on the second sheet of card.

Play the game

Ask the child to make a robot's face by arranging the shapes on the large square. He

could for instance use two triangles for eyes, a square for a nose and a rectangle for a mouth.

When the child has completed one face he can use the shapes again to create a completely different face. Do remember to name the shapes as the child plays with them.

Shape pictures

Collect together:

- old colourful magazines
- scissors
- glue and a glue brush
- a sheet of paper

Play the game

Together with your child, decide on a simple shape like a square or a circle. Look through the old magazines and see if you can find your shape in any of the pictures. For example, pictures of clocks and wheels are circles.

Cut out as many of the chosen shapes as you can find and stick them on to the paper.

A solids table

It is difficult for very young children to think in terms of three dimensions. They often call a sphere (i.e. a ball) a circle, or a cube (i.e. a play brick) a square. A table entirely devoted to the display of a particular solid shape can help them to understand, feel and see the difference between two dimensional and three dimensional objects.

For example, if you decide that your table is going to be devoted to 'cylinders', you can ask your child to help you collect together some tin cans, the centre from a toilet roll, a rolling pin, a tumbler, and so on. Place the collection on a

convenient table or window ledge and put a label with the word 'cylinders' next to the display. After a few days start again with a different solid shape, e.g. cubes.

Shapes lotto

(To make a game for two players)

Collect together:

- 2 large sheets of 30cm by 20cm card
- 12 pieces of 9cm by 9cm card
- a ruler
- a felt tip pen

Make the game

1 Divide the two large sheets of card into six equal sections. Each section should be 10cm by 10cm.
2 In each section draw a shape, i.e. a triangle, a square, a circle, a rectangle, an oval and a hexagon.

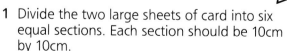

3 On the twelve small cards draw the shapes again. (Draw each shape twice.)

Play the game

Each player takes a large card. The small cards are spread picture side down between the players. Each player takes a turn at lifting a small card and, if she can, she uses it to cover an identical shape on her card. You could also add the rule that all shapes must be named before they are covered.

The winner is the first one to cover all her shapes.

Shapes I spy

Play the game

The modern world is full of recognisable shapes and you can use them to play the traditional game of I spy with your child. Simply choose an object (clock face) which has the desired shape (circle) and play the I spy game.

"I spy with my little eye a circle." (It helps tremendously if you also draw the shape in the air with your finger.)

Your child must then look around the room or outside for the correct circular object.

Shape stickers

Collect together:

● colourful paper cut into various shapes
● Blu-Tack

Play the game

Take the shapes and the Blu-Tack and together

with your child go for a walk around the house. Whenever you see an appropriately shaped object ask the child to stick a shape sticker on to it, e.g. a clock face could have a circle sticker. Each time your child uses a sticker remind them of the name of the shape.

After a few days the child could be asked to 'hunt' down all the shape stickers and bring them back to you. It is best to 'hunt' one shape at a time

Make a house

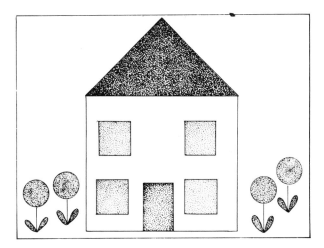

(To make a game for two players)

Collect together:

● 4 sheets of 25cm by 25cm card
● a ruler
● a pencil
● a felt tip pen
● scissors
● crayons
● a dice or number spinner

Make the game

1 On two of the sheets of card draw an identical simple house. Include the following shapes in the design: 'square' windows, a 'rectangular' door, a 'triangular' roof, and some 'circle' flowers in the garden.

2 Use the second two pieces of card to cut out a set of the shapes you have used on the houses. Make sure that the cut-out shapes are exactly the same size as the house shapes. Colour the cut-outs, using a separate colour for each shape.

3 Each cut out shape is given a value, e.g. squares = 1, circles = 2, etc. It might help your child to remember the number if you print it on to the back of each shape.

Play the game

Each player is given a house card. The players take turns at throwing the dice and taking the cut-out shapes whose numbers correspond to the thrown numbers. The player places the cut out on top of the same shape on his card. If the dice shows an unwanted number, e.g. a 6, the player misses a turn.

The winner is the first one to cover his house with cut out shapes.

Kim's shapes

Collect together:

- a tray
- an assortment of cut out card shapes

Play the game

Sit with your child on the carpet with the tray of shapes in front of you. Look carefully at the shapes for a few minutes with your child and spend a little time naming them.

Ask your child to close her eyes while you remove and hide one of the shapes. On opening her eyes she should try to guess which of the shapes has been removed.

With very young children it is best to start with a low number of shapes but as they become more proficient you can make the game harder by adding a second attribute to the shapes used, for example you could make a set of shapes in two sizes, i.e. large squares and small squares.

Beach shapes

Play the game

Here is a game to play next time you spend the day on the beach. Draw some large shapes in the sand and play the game of 'Simon says'.

For example "Simon says jump into the square, Simon says hop into the circle, run into the triangle!"

Your child should carry out the instructions correctly (and find the right shape) whenever you use the words 'Simon says'. If you do not use the words 'Simon says' he should stand still.

Printing shapes

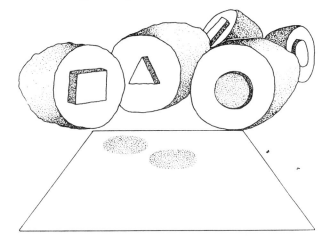

Collect together:

- a few potato print potatoes with different shapes cut into the printing surface
- sheets of paper
- coloured paints and paint brushes

Play the game

Give your child the print potatoes and the paint and encourage her to print out shape patterns on to the sheets of paper.

The printed shapes can also make pictures, for example a tree can be produced by printing a 'square' print tree trunk and 'circle' print leaves.

A feelie box

Collect together:

- a large cardboard box with circular hole cut in one side
- a selection of differently shaped objects, e.g. a long thin pencil, a round ball, a curved banana, a soft square handkerchief

Play the game

Place the objects in the box and close the lid. Simply ask your child to push his hand through the hole in the side of the box and feel the objects inside. This activity by itself is exciting and it is also a valuable experience for your child as he will become more aware of his sense of touch without the aid of sight.

Later you can ask him to describe what he can feel or to find a particular object for you.

 # Time

A time diary

Collect together:

- an artist's plain paper sketch pad or some plain white paper stapled together
- a felt tip pen
- a jam jar lid to draw round
- crayons

Make the diary

On the top left hand corner of each page, draw round the jam jar lid and print a clock face without hands.

How to use the diary

Talk to the child about her day. What time does she get up in the morning? (Pick the nearest hour. Don't bother to introduce half hours or minutes at this stage.) If the answer is 7.00, let the child watch while you draw the hands on the first clock in the diary to show 7.00. Ask the child to draw a picture of herself getting up at seven underneath the clock.

Throughout the rest of the day make entries

in the time diary. I would suggest you include what your child is doing at 10.00, 12.00, 5.00 and so on until bed time.

If your child is out for part of the day, shopping or at playgroup, she can fill in the time diary when she returns home

A Coco the Clown calendar

Collect together:

- a large sheet of paper, 50cm by 30cm
- 3 small paper plates
- 3 strips of 5cm by 1cm card
- 3 brass paper fasteners
- a felt tip pen
- a pencil
- a ruler
- crayons
- scissors

Make the game

1 Using the pencil and ruler divide the first paper plate into 7 and then use the felt tip pen to print out the names of the days of the week on the outside edge of each section.

Divide the second plate into 4 sections and print out the names of the four seasons in each one and finally divide the last plate into 12 sections and print out the names of the months of the year.

2 On the large sheet of paper draw a large clown shape. Make sure his body is large enough to contain all three plates and then use the crayons to give him some colour. Your child will probably enjoy helping you to do this.

3 Use the scissors to cut the three 5cm by 1cm strips into arrow shapes.

4 Attach an arrow to the centre of each plate with a brass paper fastener and then attach the plates to the clown by pressing the fasteners through the clown's body. Do make sure that the arrows can move.

Play the game

Hang the clown picture on a convenient wall or door and ask the child to point each arrow towards the appropriate section. Repeat this at intervals through the week and through the year.

A paper plate clock

Collect together:

- a large paper plate
- a brass paper fastner
- scissors
- a felt tip pen
- a ruler
- a pencil
- 2 strips of 10cm by 2cm card

To make the clock

1 Draw a simple clock face, minus hands, on the front of the paper plate.

2 Cut out a long hand and a short hand from the pieces of card and attach the hands to the centre of the clock face with brass paper fastener.

To use the clock

To begin with, talk about the numbers around the outside of the clock and then move on to show the position of the hands for simple times such as 1.00, 2.00 etc. At specific times during the day ask your child to put the hands in the right position on the clock, e.g. at 9.00 playgroup time, 12.00 lunchtime or 7.00 storytime.

Using a timer

Many cookers have a timer attached but if you can buy a mechanical egg timer you will find it a very useful piece of equipment for your child.

The timer can be used in a variety of ways to help your child learn how to estimate time, e.g. if your child is slow at getting dressed in the morning, ask him to beat the bell by dressing before it rings. Tell him how many minutes you are setting on the timer before he starts to dress. At other times he could try to complete a jigsaw before the bell rings, or drink a glass of milk. You could set it to ring at bedtime or when his favourite TV programme starts, and of course cooking his boiled egg for tea is greatly assisted by the use of the timer.

Each time it is used, carefully explain how many minutes are involved. In this way your child should learn what 'in a minute' really means and he will build up some understanding of the length of time.

Obstacle races

Play the game

This game can be played either indoors or out. Simply create an obstacle course with pieces of furniture or garden equipment and ask your child to compete with herself to see how many times she can complete a circuit in a given time.

Not only does this activity help her judge the length of a specified time and the 'number' of times she can complete the course but it's an ideal chance for boisterous children to work off some of their energy.

The chatterbox game

Play the game

This game is based on a popular radio programme.

Ideally you need several members of the family to play the game and either a watch with a minute hand or a wind up minute timer.

One person acts as time keeper and score keeper.

The idea is for each contestant to talk about a subject, for example, 'dogs' or to tell a fairy story, for one minute without stopping or pausing.

If the contestant is able to talk for one minute he scores a point, but if he stops or pauses, the next person in line takes over and attempts to complete the minute, thus gaining the point.

At the end of one minute the next person in line has a turn and the subject can be changed. If a fairy story is being told the next contestant must add more details to the existing tale. The winner is the one with the most points after playing the game for an agreed length of time.

A seasons collage

Collect together:

- a long strip of paper (wallpaper lining paper is ideal)
- glue and a glue brush
- a felt tip pen
- together with your child make a collection of suitably seasonal pictures and objects, e.g.

Winter
A holly leaf, cotton wool, old Christmas cards, silver glitter, tin foil and shiny red paper.

Spring
Yellow and pink tissue paper, pictures of spring flowers and baby animals, old Easter cards, pieces of ribbon, shiny green paper and crushed egg shells.

Summer
Small shells or pasta shells, sand, old postcards, old bus and train tickets, pictures of ice-cream and fizzy drinks, gold paper.

Autumn
Orange and brown tissue paper leaves, twigs, pictures of bonfires and fireworks (the child could draw these herself), pictures of apples and other fruits.

To make the collage

Use the felt tip pen to divide the strip of paper into 4 equal sections and at the top of each section write the name of one of the four seasons.

Provide the child with one set of the seasonal objects at a time and ask her to stick these into the appropriate section. Talk about the different seasons as she works. The topics could include the weather, the clothes you wear, the food you might eat. etc.

A time for tea book

Collect together:

- a scrap book
- glue and a glue brush
- scissors
- felt tip pens
- the wrappers and labels from as many different foods as possible

Play the game

Devote several pages of the scrapbook to each meal of the day.

Breakfast . . . 8.o.clock
Breaktime . . . 10.o.clock
Lunchtime . . . 12.o.clock
Teatime . . . 4.o.clock
Suppertime . . . 6.o.clock

Help your child to draw a clock for every mealtime on the top of each page and to draw the hands of the clock in the correct position. Write the name of the meal at the side of each clock.

Ask your child to stick appropriate cut out labels and food wrappers on to the correct pages, for example, the front of a fish fingers box could be cut out and stuck on to a teatime page. If your child is unable to obtain a wrapper from a certain food i.e. a lunchtime apple, ask her to draw a picture of the food directly on to the page.

At the end of the day you can count up how many different foods she has eaten and if you keep filling the scrap book for a week she can see for herself how many varieties of food make up her diet.

Measurement

Measuring with your body

Here is a question you might ask your child.

"I wonder how many strides you take when you walk down the hall? Let's count them and see."

After counting her strides along the hall, why not count how many she takes to cross the living room? Which took the most strides, hall or living room?

In this activity and in answering your questions, your child is discovering something of simple measurement. Indeed long before formal measuring devices were introduced, people used their bodies to measure in much the same way.

You don't have to restrict yourself to strides. Any part of the child's body could be used. e.g. "Let's see how many thumbs we can fit along this book?"

You needn't confine yourself to inside the house either. Count the number of strides between lamp posts on the way to the shops.

How tall is teddy?

Collect together:

- 5 or 6 pieces of 20cm by 20cm card
- a collection of identical small objects, e.g. paper clips or small bricks
- a felt tip pen

Make the game

Draw an outline shape of an animal or toy on each of the pieces of card. Make sure that the picture starts at the bottom of each card, i.e. teddy's feet should be right on the bottom edge.

Play the game

Give the child the collection of small items, e.g. small bricks, and one of the cards. Starting at the bottom of the card, the bricks are placed next to each other in a line until the top of the picture is reached. How many bricks did it take to reach the top of teddy?

How tall am I?

Collect together:

- a long strip of card, approx 30cm wide and at least 150cm long
- a ruler
- a felt tip pen
- crayons
- Blu-Tack

Make the game

1 Draw a line down the centre of the strip and mark it in centimetres. For the first metre it is only really necessary to mark every 10cm.
2 Decorate the strip with pictures. It is always fun to reflect on the changes in your child as he grows and so the pictures at the bottom of the strip could feature baby toys and as you move up the strip you can include his current interests and pastimes. Your child will obviously love to help you to do this.

3 Stick the strip to the wall with Blu-Tack.

Play the game

Every few months ask your child to take his shoes off and stand against the strip. Record his height by drawing an arrow next to the cm mark and write down the date.

Children love to see themselves growing and just to see the marks on the chart moving upwards is very exciting for them.

Using string as a measure

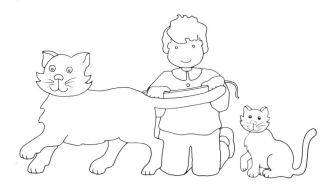

Collect together:

- a ball of string
- scissors
- paper
- a pencil
- Sellotape

Play the game

To start with, use the ball of string to measure different parts of your·child's body. For example, when measuring his head, wrap the string around the top of the head and carefully cut the string where it meets together. You could also

measure his wrist, ankle, finger, arm, waist and chest. To make identifying the strings easier you can mark each one with a label made from the paper and Sellotape.

When you have finished measuring, lay all the strings side by side so that the child can see for himself which is the longest and shortest. You can later move on to measuring other members of the family and comparing their sizes.

String can also be used to measure toys, books, shoes, bananas, forks, the letter box and indeed absolutely anything. At this stage there is no need to mention centimetres.

Using scales

Collect together:

- traditional kitchen scales. The type with two pans.
- a collection of small objects, e.g. acorns, conkers, toy farm animals, a paper bag full of cotton wool, toy bricks, etc.

To use the scales

Show the child how to balance the scales and then set him some simple questions, e.g. Which is heavier the bag of cotton wool or the brick? How many conkers do you need to balance the toy car?

Of course children also love to help to use the scales during cooking activities and when time permits they should be allowed to measure out the ingredients.

Bathtime fun

To become aware of the concepts 'full'and 'empty', 'too much', and 'not enough', to provide a focus for early measurement, simple counting, and an opportunity to learn all about the different properties of water, there is no better place for the child to play, than in his bath.

All you need to provide is a warm bath, lots of differently shaped containers such as plastic tubing, a sieve, a funnel, plus of course appropriate language to help the child understand the concepts he is being presented with.

To make the play exciting some of the containers, for example empty plastic bottles, could have lots of small holes cut into them, while other could have simple measurement marks drawn on their sides. Young children almost invariably love to play with water and very soon become absorbed in water play. Water is one of the most natural, stimulating and valuble learning aids.

Giants

Play the game

Take a piece of chalk and go outside with your child. Find a large area suitable for chalk drawing, such as the driveway, and help your child to draw as large a giant as she can.

When the giant is complete you can use him for some simple feet measurement. For example, how many strides does it take to walk all the way round the outside of the giant? How many feet will fit along the giant's arm or leg? How tall is he? How many strides between the giant's nose and the tip of his finger?

Measuring rain drops

Collect together:

● a straight stick or piece of wood

Play the game

After some heavy rain ask your child to put on her wellington boots and go outside with you to measure the rain drops in the puddles. Ask your child to dip the stick into the middle of each puddle and to measure how deep it is by counting how many fingers will fit along the wet mark on the stick.

Children love splashing about in water and will enjoy dipping the measuiring stick into all the puddles in order to find the deepest one.

Heavy and light

Play the game

On your return home from a food shopping trip allow your child to play with the groceries for a little while before you put them away. Ask her to balance different items in her hands and to feel which foods are the heaviest by discovering which items push her hands down more. If she has a tin of dog meat in one hand and a packet of biscuits in the other, she will soon be able to decide which is lighter and which is heavier.

If some of the items are too big to hold in her hands, give her two plastic carrier bags and suggest she balances the foods in these. Encourage her to make two sets or groups of foods, one heavy and the other light.

A sunflower race

Your child might like to have a sunflower race with other members of the family or perhaps with some of his friends.

Simply buy a packet of giant (Helianthus) sunflower seeds, choose a really sunny spot in the garden and give each child a seed to plant. As the plants need plenty of room to grow they will need to be sown at least 50cm apart. Mark each planted seed with a name label and water frequently.

Sunflowers grow very rapidly and they often need to be supported with a tall stick. Decide on a judging date during the late summer and provide a prize for the tallest flower.

If you keep the flower head seeds you will have plenty seeds for the following years competition, plus some seeds to feed to the wild birds during the winter months.

Money

A pocket money chart

	Monday	Tuesday	Wednesday	Thursday	Friday	Saturday	Sunday
2p	✔			✔	✔		
3p		✔			✔		✔
5p	✔						✔
5p			✔			✔	
10p				✔			

Collect together:

- a small piece of paper
- a large piece of paper
- a ruler
- a felt tip pen

To make the chart

1 On the small piece of paper make a list of all the little jobs that your child can do and give each job a payment price, e.g.

Putting the milk bottles out for the milkman = 2p
Feeding the dog = 3p
Tidying the bedroom = 5p

2 Divide the large sheet of paper into squares. You will need 8 squares across and as many squares down as you have jobs.
3 Missing out the first square on the top left hand side, write out the days of the week along the top of the paper.
4 Down the left hand side of the paper write out the jobs your child could do, plus the price for each one. It is also a good idea to draw a small picture of each job, e.g. a picture of a bed for tidying the bedroom.
5 Pin the chart to a convenient wall or door.

To use the chart

Each time your child completes a job she ticks the appropriate square and writes the payment price next to the tick. At the end of the week the amounts are added up and the payment is made.

Coin rubbing

Collect together:

- sheets of paper
- black wax crayons or a thick black pencil
- a handful of coins

To play the game

Give the child the coins and ask her to put them one at a time underneath the sheet of paper and then to gently rub over the top of the coin with the black crayon. The patterns and pictures on the coin will emerge through the paper.

This is a useful activity as it helps the child to recognise the different coins and if they are mounted on card they can be used as pretend money for a pretend shop.

Money

A pretend shop

The benefits of having a pretend shop for your child are enormous. A few tins and packets from the cupboard along with some fruit and vegetables, a toy till or a shoe box of money (real money or clean milk bottle tops), and a handful of simple price tickets, (nothing over 10p) provide the basis for imaginative play with a lot of learning potential.

Ask the child to arrange the stock in the shop, this will automatically involve the child in 'sorting' out the fruit and the different types of tins and packets. The price tickets can then be put on the groceries.

When buying or selling, the child will be actively involved in simple counting, recognising numbers and coins, taking away, and division. Ideally you should be around to provide the language he needs to understand the concepts he is dealing with. Simple questions from you such as "How many milk bottle tops have you got left? Have you got enough to buy this orange? Let's count these apples and see if we

can all have one each", will help your child to think about the numbers and amounts involved.

Older children could even be encouraged to keep a stock book and count the takings at the end of a session.

Fill the purse

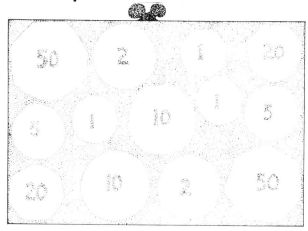

(To make a game for two players)

Collect together:

- 2 sheets of 20cm by 20cm card
- a felt tip pen
- some real money
- a money spinner. Detailed instruction on how to make a spinner can be found in the Number section, but instead of the usual numbers divide the spinner into six sections and print out the amounts, 50p, 20p, 10p, 5p, 2p, and 1p.

Make the game

1 Draw a simple purse shape on each of the sheets of card.

2 Inside each purse draw the outline shape of two 50p's, two 10p's, two 20p's, two 5p's, two 2p's and three 1p's. The simplest method of doing this is to draw round the coins themselves.

3 Print the value of each coin inside each shape.

Play the game

Each player takes a purse card. Taking turns, the players spin the money spinner and pick up the appropriate coin. The coins are used to cover the coin shapes in the purse. The first one to fill his purse with real money is the winner.

Coin sorting

Collect together:

- 6 saucers
- loose change containing 50p's, 20p's, 10p's, 5p's, 2p's and 1p's

Play the game

In the bottom of each saucer put a different coin, e.g. saucer 1 would contain a 1p, saucer 2 would contain a 2p, etc.

Give the child the loose change and ask her to sort it out for you by putting the coins in the correct saucers.

Cardboard trains

Collect together:

- lots of large empty cardboard boxes
- a thick black felt tip pen
- a long length of thick string
- scissors
- pretend or real money
- pretend train tickets

Make the game

1 Help your child make the boxes into a train by drawing wheels, levers, doors and handles on to the boxes with the felt tip pen.

2 Tie the boxes loosely together in a line, by threading thick string through a hole in the back of one box and the front of another. In this way you can make a long 'train' of boxes.

Play the game

Your child will need plenty of passengers for this game, so as well as inviting other members of the family or friends to play she may like to include several of her soft toys or dolls.

Allow your child to take turns at being passenger, train driver, ticket collector, and other station personnel.

Agree on a price for each ticket and help the children to collect and pay the fares. If using real money stick to simple amounts.

It can be great fun deciding where to travel to, especially if you take along a picnic for the journey.